James Brewerton

ASTERIX AND THE NORMANS

TEXT BY GOSCINNY

DRAWINGS BY UDERZO

TRANSLATED BY ANTHEA BELL AND DEREK HOCKRIDGE

HODDER AND STOUGHTON
LONDON SYDNEY AUCKLAND TORONTO

ASTERIX IN OTHER LANGUAGES

Australia	Hodder & Stoughton Children's Books, Mill Road, Dunton Green, Sevenoaks, Kent, TN13 2YJ, England
Austria	Delta Verlag, Postfach 1215, 7 Stuttgart 1, R.F.A.
Belgium	Dargaud Benelux, 3 rue Kindermans, 1050 Brussels
Brazil	Cedibra, rua Filomena Nunes 162, Rio de Janeiro
Canada	Dargaud Canada Ltee, 307 Benjamin Hudon, St-Laurent-Montreal PQ, H4 N1 J1
Denmark	Gutenberghus Bladene, Vognmagergade 11, 1148 Copenhagen K
Finland	Sanoma Osakeyhtio, Ludviginkatu 2-10,00130 Helsinki 12
France	Dargaud Editeur, 12 rue Blaise-Pascal, P.O. Box 155, 92201 Neuilly Sur Seine
	(Breton) Armor Diffusion, 59 rue Duhamel, 35100 Rennes
	(Langue d'Oc) Societe Toulousaine Du Livre, Avenue de Larrieu, 31094 Toulouse
German Federal Republic	Delta Verlag, Postfach 1215, 7 Stuttgart 1, R.F.A.
Greece	Anglo Hellenic Agency, 5 Koumpari Street, Athens 138
Holland	Dargaud Benelux, 3 rue Kindermans, 1050 Brussels
Hong Kong	Hodder & Stoughton Children's Books, Mill Road, Dunton Green, Sevenoaks, Kent, TN13 2YJ, England
Iceland	Fjolvi Hf, Njorvasund 15a, Reykjavik
Indonesia	Yayasan Aspirasi Pemuda, Jalan Kebon Kacang, Raya 1, Flat 3, Tingkat 111, Jakarta
Italy	Arnoldo Mondadori Editore, Via Bianca de Savoia 20 20122, Milan
Latin America	Ediciones Junior S.A., 386 Aragon, Barcelona 9, Spain
New Zealand	Hodder & Stoughton Children's Books, Mill Road, Dunton Green, Sevenoaks, Kent, TN13 2YJ, England
Norway	A/S Hjemmet (Gutenberghus Group) Kristian den 4 des Gate 13, Oslo 1
Portugal	Meriberica, rua d. Filipa de Vilherna 4-5°, Lisbon
Roman Empire	*(Latin)* Delta Verlag, Postfach 1215, 7 Stuttgart 1, R.F.A.
South Africa	*(English)* Hodder & Stoughton Children's Books, Mill Road, Dunton Green, Sevenoaks, Kent, TN13 2YJ, England
Spain	Ediciones Junior S.A., 386 Aragon, Barcelona 9
Sweden	Hemmets Journal Forlag (Gutenberghus Group) Fack 200 22 Malmo
Switzerland	Interpress S.A., En Budron, B, 1052 Le Mont/Lausanne
Turkey	Kervan Kitabcilik, Serefendi Sokagi 31, Cagaloglu-Istanbul
Wales	*(Welsh)* Gwasg Y Dref Wen, 28 Church Road, Yr Eglwys Newydd, Cardiff
Yugoslavia	Nip Forum Vojvode Misica 1-3, 2100 Novi Sad

 First published in Great Britain 1978. Second impression 1978. ISBN 0 340 22287 5. Printed in Belgium for Hodder & Stoughton Children's Books, a division of Hodder & Stoughton Ltd, Mill Road, Dunton Green, Sevenoaks, Kent TN13 2YJ (Editorial Office: 47 Bedford Square, London WC1B 3DP) by Henri Proost & Cie, Turnhout.

The year is 50 BC. Gaul is entirely occupied by the Romans. Well, not entirely... One small village of indomitable Gauls still holds out against the invaders. And life is not easy for the Roman legionaries who garrison the fortified camps of Totorum, Aquarium, Laudanum and Compendium...

a few of the Gauls

Asterix, the hero of these adventures. A shrewd, cunning little warrior; all perilous missions are immediately entrusted to him. Asterix gets his superhuman strength from the magic potion brewed by the druid Getafix...

Obelix, Asterix's inseparable friend. A menhir delivery-man by trade; addicted to wild boar. Obelix is always ready to drop everything and go off on a new adventure with Asterix – so long as there's wild boar to eat, and plenty of fighting.

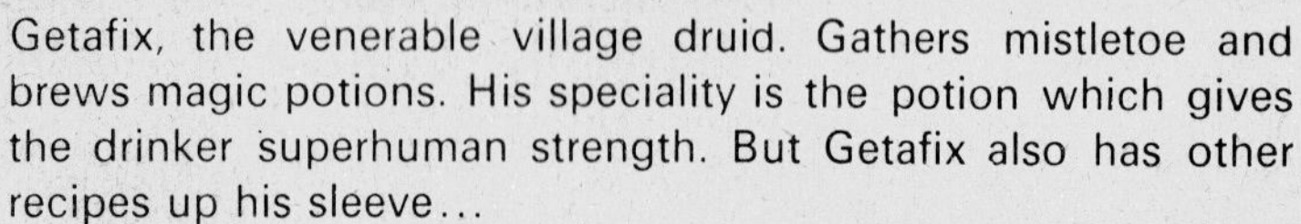

Getafix, the venerable village druid. Gathers mistletoe and brews magic potions. His speciality is the potion which gives the drinker superhuman strength. But Getafix also has other recipes up his sleeve...

Cacofonix, the bard. Opinion is divided as to his musical gifts. Cacofonix thinks he's a genius. Everyone else thinks he's unspeakable. But so long as he doesn't speak, let alone sing, everybody likes him...

Finally, Vitalstatistix, the chief of the tribe. Majestic, brave and hot-tempered, the old warrior is respected by his men and feared by his enemies. Vitalstatistix himself has only one fear; he is afraid the sky may fall on his head tomorrow. But as he always says, 'Tomorrow never comes.'

ANOTHER PEACEFUL DAY HAS DAWNED IN THE LITTLE VILLAGE WE KNOW SO WELL...
LOOK, DARLING! THE ARMS AND ARMOUR FIRM HAS SENT ITS MAIL ORDER CATALOGUE AT LAST!
WHY, THERE'S POSTALDISTRIX THE POSTMAN!

NOTHING FOR US, POSTALDISTRIX?
NO. I HAVE A LETTER FOR CHIEF VITALSTATISTIX TO DELIVER, AND THAT'S ALL!
WE'LL GO WITH YOU.
G.P.O.

CAN YOU SEND MENHIRS BY POST?
YES, BUT IT'S A GOOD IDEA TO REGISTER THEM IN CASE THEY GET LOST.

A LETTER FROM LUTETIA, O CHIEF VITALSTATISTIX!
OH, THAT MUST BE FROM MY BROTHER DOUBLEHELIX ...THOUGH HE DOESN'T ENGRAVE VERY OFTEN!

OH!
NOTHING GRAVE ENGRAVED THERE, I HOPE?

NO, MY BROTHER DOUBLEHELIX HAS A SON CALLED JUSTFORKIX, AND IT SEEMS MY NEPHEW IS GETTING A BIT SOFT LIVING IN LUTETIA. DOUBLEHELIX IS SENDING HIM HERE FOR A HOLIDAY. HE WANTS US TO MAKE A MAN OF HIM!

I HOPE I CAN COUNT ON YOU, FRIENDS?
BY THE TIME WE'RE THROUGH WITH HIM HE'LL BE HUNTING BOAR WITH HIS BARE HANDS!
YOU MEAN THERE'S SOME OTHER WAY TO DO IT?

WATCH OUT!
BY TOUTATIS!
HE'S CRAZY!
CLUCK CLUCK
YELP YELP YELP

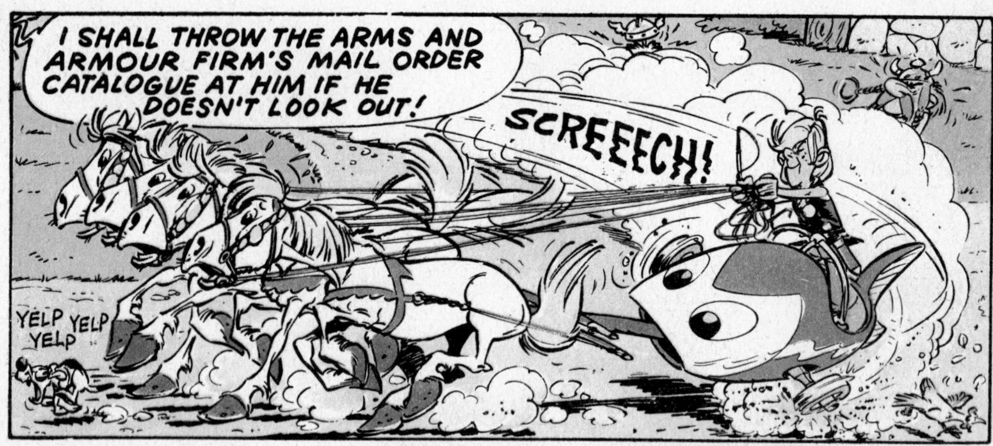
I SHALL THROW THE ARMS AND ARMOUR FIRM'S MAIL ORDER CATALOGUE AT HIM IF HE DOESN'T LOOK OUT!
SCREEECH!
YELP YELP YELP

HI, UNCLE! I'M YOUR NEPHEW JUSTFORKIX!
?!

ER... VERY NICE TO SEE YOU, JUSTFORKIX... LET ME INTRODUCE ASTERIX AND OBELIX...
I'VE NEVER SEEN A CHARIOT LIKE THAT BEFORE...
2A

NO, YOU WOULDN'T GET MANY OF THESE AROUND HERE... IT'S A SPORTS CHARIOT MADE IN MEDIOLANUM*...
*MILAN

RIGHT, LET'S START.
START WHAT?

START MAKING A MAN OF HIM, OF COURSE! THE WAY TO START MAKING A MAN OF HIM IS TO START THUMPING HIM!
NO, NO, THAT'S NOT THE WAY.

OH, AND JUST HOW DOES MISTER ASTERIX THINK WE'RE GOING TO START MAKING A MAN OF HIM IF WE DON'T START THUMPING HIM SO AS TO START MAKING A MAN OF HIM?
WE WANT HIM TO TRUST US!

WE'RE GOING TO HOLD A BALL IN YOUR HONOUR, JUSTFORKIX!
YOU PEASANTS DANCE OUT HERE IN THE STYX?*
*GLOOMY CLASSICAL ALLUSION

HOW QUAINT!
YOU KNOW, OBELIX, I'M NOT SURE YOU WEREN'T RIGHT ABOUT THUMPING HIM!
SEE?
WOOF!
2B

YES, WE'LL HAVE A BALL FOR MY NEPHEW... THAT'S A GOOD NOTION, ASTERIX.
I'M NOT SURE HE APPRECIATES ...
YOUR FIRST BALL, DOGMATIX! IT'S A GREAT OCCASION!
YOU CAN PLAY, BUT YOU CAN'T SING. IF YOU SING I SHALL BASH YOU!
IGNORAMUS.

WHAT WAS THAT?
URGGH!

OH, I THOUGHT YOU SPOKE...
PLOINK! PLOINK!

LET'S TRIP THE LIGHT FANTASTIX. COMING?
YOU TWO GO. I WANT TO WATCH.
YOU'LL ASK A GIRL TO DANCE FOR ME, WON'T YOU, ASTERIX?

MAY MY FRIEND AND I HAVE THE PLEASURE OF THIS DANCE?
TEEHEEHEE!
OOOH, I SAY!
?

BONG! BONG!
WOOF! WOOF!

NO! NO! NO! OLD-TIME DANCING MAY BE ALL RIGHT FOR GOLDEN OLDIES, BUT LET ME SHOW YOU WHAT WE GET UP TO IN THE CATACOMBS OF LUTETIA THESE DAYS!
BANG!

I BEG YOUR PARDON!

THE ROLLING MENHIRS!
?

PLOINK!
PLOINK!
!?!
?!?

PLOINK!
YEEEEAH
PLOINK!

HEY, OBELIX, DID YOU SEE TH...
TZOIIING!
DONG!

PLOINK!
PLINK!

OBELIX!?

TZOIIIING!
SURELY A MENHIR MAKER'S ENTITLED TO A BIT OF ROCK, ASTERIX...

...ANY WAY, WE MUST KEEP UP WITH ANCIENT TIMES!
HARFF! HARFF! HARFF!

STOP IT! THIS IS TOO MUCH! WE'VE HAD ENOUGH OF YOUR BARBARIC RHYTHM! LET'S GET BACK TO OUR GOOD OLD TRADITIONAL FOLKSONGS.
?
DOIIING!

...WITH ASTERIX, OBELIX, OLD UNCLE VITALSTATISTIX AND ALL...
DOING!
DOING!
POM! TOM! POM!

COME ON, LET'S GO!
I'VE GOT A MENHIR TO FINISH...
MUMMY EXPECTS ME HOME!
POING!

SAY, YOU'RE GREAT! YOU'RE WASTING YOUR TIME HERE; YOU'D GO DOWN MUCH BETTER IN LUTETIA AT THE PALACE OF VARIETIX... AUDIENCES DON'T STRIKE THERE!
YOU THINK I'D MAKE A HIT IN LUTETIA?

WHILE ALL THIS IS GOING ON IN GAUL, LET US TRAVEL FAR AWAY, TO THE NORTHERN LANDS WHERE WINTERS ARE HARD AND THE NIGHT LASTS FOR MONTHS ON END... LANDS INHABITED BY THE NORSEMEN, OR NORMANS, AS THE PEOPLE OF GAUL KNEW THEM. THEY ARE GREAT CONQUERORS...
WE GIVE THE GAULS A MISS FOR ONCE AND THAT LOT MAKE A NORMAN CONQUEST OF US!

THEY WORSHIP THOR, THE GOD OF WAR, AND ODIN, WHO INVITES WARRIORS SLAIN IN BATTLE TO FEAST WITH HIM IN VALHALLA...
WON'T!

AND THEY DO NOT KNOW THE MEANING OF FEAR!
IF YOU DON'T FINISH YOUR NICE CREAM SOUP THE TROLL WILL COME AND EAT YOU UP!
BY THOR, THAT'S A LAUGH!

THIS IS A NUISANCE, SINCE NOT ONLY ARE THE CHILDREN NOT SCARED OF TROLLS, BUT AS FEAR OF THE AUTHORITIES ENCOURAGES PRUDENCE, NORSE ROADS ARE FAR FROM SAFE...
WHAT DO YOU MEAN BY IT, TRYING TO PASS A FOUR-REINDEER-POWER POLICE CHARIOT AT THE TOP OF A HILL???
SO WHAT? MINE'S A NORSE-DRAWN CHARIOT!

...AND IT IS PRACTICALLY IMPOSSIBLE TO CURE HICCUPS...
HAVE YOU OR HAVE YOU NOT FINISHED HICCUPPING?
HIC! NO. HIC! WHY DO YOU ASK?
5A

HOPING TO LEARN THE MEANING OF FEAR, OLD NORSE SCHOLARS CARRY OUT SCIENTIFIC EXPERIMENTS...

FEEL ANYTHING?
NO FEAR SO FAR, ONLY PAIN. HAVE ANOTHER GO.

SO CHIEF OLAF TIMANDAHAF ASSEMBLES HIS MEN...
WE CAN'T GO ON LIKE THIS! EVEN THE WEAKEST OF NATIONS KNOW ABOUT FEAR AND BEING FRIGHTENED... BUT NOT US!

AND WE PRIDE OURSELVES ON KNOWING EVERYTHING! EVERYTHING!
THUMP! THUMP! THUMP!
BUT LISTEN, O TIMANDAHAF, WHAT USE IS THIS THING FEAR THAT WE DON'T UNDERSTAND?

I'VE HEARD THAT FEAR LENDS YOU WINGS, BY ODIN. ONCE WE CAN FLY LIKE BIRDS WE'LL STICK AT NOTHING.
5-B
BY THOR!
BY ODIN!
BY GUM...

I SUGGEST WE START OUT TODAY FOR THE LANDS WHERE PEOPLE KNOW THE MEANING OF FEAR! WE'LL DEAL DEATH AND DESTRUCTION IF NECESSARY. BUT WE MUST AND WILL LEARN THE SECRET!
HEAR! HEAR!
WE'RE WITH YOU!
LONG LIVE CHIEF TIMANDAHAF!

AND I PROMISE YOU, WE SHALL COME HOME TO TELL AN ADMIRING WORLD: THE NORMANS KNOW THE MEANING OF FEAR! THE NORMANS ARE MORE FRIGHTENED THAN YOU!

NOW FOR OUR NATIONAL BEVERAGE, APPLE BRANDY DRUNK FROM THE SKULLS OF OUR ENEMIES! IT'S A VERY HEADY LIQUOR.

SO THAT SAME NIGHT, I. E. THREE WEEKS LATER, A MIGHTY NORMAN LONGSHIP FULL OF FIERCE WARRIORS SETS OFF ON ITS UNUSUAL VOYAGE OF SCIENTIFIC DISCOVERY...
WHAT SHORE ARE WE MAKING FOR, O TIMANDAHAF?
I CHOSE ONE AT RANDOM, O NESCAF. WE'RE MAKING FOR GAUL.

WHICH SHOULD TEACH US ALL TO DISTRUST RANDOM SAMPLES, SINCE AS WE KNOW THE GAULS ARE NOT TOO KNOWLEDGEABLE ABOUT THE MEANING OF FEAR EITHER. IN FACT, THEY FEAR ONLY ONE THING, THE SKY FALLING ON THEIR HEADS, AND THEY DON'T LET THAT KEEP THEM AWAKE AT NIGHT...
GET UP, LAZY! THE ROOSTER HAS CROWED TO LET US KNOW IT'S DAY!
RIGHT, THEN YOU DON'T NEED ME ANY MORE...

THIS IS THE TIME I GO TO BED IN LUTETIA.
OBELIX, HOW ABOUT HELPING HIM GET UP?
CAN I, ASTERIX? CAN I?

OUOUAAAAAH!

PLAF!
HE SEEMS TO HAVE GOT OUT OF BED THE WRONG SIDE.
6 II

YOU'VE GOT NO RIGHT TO MAKE ME GET UP SO EARLY! I'M SUPPOSED TO BE ON HOLIDAY.
SO YOU ARE! WE'RE GOING DOWN TO THE BEACH!

THE BEACH? BUT IT'S RAINING!
IT MIGHT BE RAIN IN THE SOUTH... HERE IT'S JUST A LITTLE BRACING DAMPNESS IN THE AIR...

AND GETTING MORE BRACING ALL THE TIME!
COME ON, LET'S HAVE A RACE! LAST MAN TO THE ROCK IS JULIUS CAESAR!
GLAC!

READY... STEADY...
WHOOSH!
GO!

PAF!
WE'VE WON!
IT DOESN'T COUNT! YOU CHEATED, BOTH OF YOU!

OH YES, IT DOES COUNT! BUT OF COURSE MISTER ASTERIX DOESN'T LIKE LOSING!
WOOF! WOOF!

WELL, NEVER MIND. HE'S JULIUS CAESAR!

I WONDER WHAT WOULD INTEREST HIM...
WHO CARES? WE'RE OFF TO LOOK FOR OYSTERS!

LISTEN, JUSTFORKIX...

OH!... OOH!... OOOOH!
IS THIS SOME NEW LUTETIAN DANCE OF YOURS?

SEE THAT SHIP? OVER THERE!
SO THERE'S A SHIP OVER THERE! WHAT ABOUT IT?

IT'S A NORSE LONGSHIP! THE NORMANS ARE TERRIBLE! A LOT OF BLOODTHIRSTY PIRATES!!

OH, YOU THINK SO? WELL, DON'T GET SO WORKED UP. WE'LL GO AND TELL THE OTHERS BACK IN THE VILLAGE...
SCRATH! SCRATCH!

OH, GLAD TO SEE YOU, OBELIX... SEE THAT SAIL OVER THERE?

HE SAYS THEY'RE PIRATES...

GOODY!
NO, NO, OBELIX! COME BACK! WE MUST GO AND TELL THE OTHERS!
SPLOSH!
SPLOSH!
SPLOSH!
WOOF! WOOF!

BUT WHAT ABOUT THE PIRATES OVER THERE?
THAT'S WHY WE HAVE TO GO BACK TO THE VILLAGE!

WHAT'S THE GOOD OF LIVING BY THE SEASIDE IF YOU NEVER GET ANY FUN OUT OF IT?
?

THEY'RE COMING! THEY'RE COMING!
THESE LUTETIANS ARE CRAZY! THEY START RUNNING AFTER THE RACE IS OVER... WELL, I'M NOT RUNNING ANY MORE! I FEEL A BIT HEAVY AFTER EATING SO MANY DOZENS OF OYSTERS.

OBELIX, I'VE TOLD YOU BEFORE... OYSTERS ARE LIKE NUTS, YOU ONLY EAT THE INSIDE.
PERSONALLY I EAT NUTS SHELL AND ALL, THE SAME WAY I EAT OYSTERS.

THE NOR... THE NOR... THE NORM...!
SEE, THAT'S LUTETIANS FOR YOU! THEY'RE ALWAYS IN A HURRY IN LUTETIA... JUST CAN'T TAKE LIFE AS IT COMES!
LUTETIA'S ALL RIGHT FOR A VISIT, BUT I DON'T FANCY LIVING THERE.

OH, I WAS LOOKING FOR YOU. I'VE BEEN THINKING ABOUT THE HIT I MIGHT MAKE IN LUTE...
CLUCK!

CLU...EEEK!

WHAT'S THE MATTER WITH HIM?
IT SEEMS THE NORMANS WANT TO INVADE US.

WE'RE OFF TO SEE THE CHIEF ABOUT IT. JUSTFORKIX WILL BE THERE BY NOW.
GOOD. I WANT TO ASK HIM ABOUT THE PALACE OF VARIETIX

SOON AFTERWARDS.
YOU TWO GO AND SEE WHAT THE NORMANS ARE DOING. IF THEY'RE LANDING, WE THROW THEM BACK INTO THE SEA.
DO YOU THINK THEY'LL LAND, ASTERIX? HEY, DO YOU REALLY THINK SO?
I'LL GO AND MAKE A LITTLE MAGIC POTION, JUST IN CASE...
PSST... I WANT A WORD WITH YOU...

WELL, NORMANS APART, DO YOU LIKE IT HERE? NOT FEELING HOMESICK?

LIS... LISTEN, DO YOU KNOW WHO THE NORMANS ARE?
OF COURSE! THEY'RE FIERCE FIGHTERS, AND LIKE US THEY DON'T KNOW THE MEANING OF FEAR!

WE MAY LIVE IN THE PROVINCES, MY BOY, BUT THAT DOESN'T MEAN WE'RE OUT OF TOUCH!
CRAZY! THEY'RE ALL CRAZY!
RIGHT, CAN WE HAVE A TALK ABOUT MY FUTURE NOW?
9 IX

LET'S GET BACK TO THE BEACH AND SEE WHAT THE NORMANS ARE DOING.
HOW ABOUT TRICKING THEM INTO LANDING, ASTERIX? HOW ABOUT IT, EH?

BUT THERE IS NO NEED FOR ANY TRICKS ... TO THE SOUND OF THEIR SAVAGE WAR-CRIES, THE NORMAN CONQUERORS ARE LANDING IN GAUL!
SEE THE CONQUERING NORMANS COME!!

WE'LL PITCH CAMP ON THIS BEACH! START DIGGING HOLES FOR THE TENT PEGS. I WANT EVERY NORMAN FULFILLING HIS NORM!

PSYCHOPAF! EPITAF! CENOTAF! TRANSPORTCAF! CHIFFCHAF! NESCAF! GET DOWN TO WORK!
HMHMTEEHEE!
SSH, OBELIX!

BUT OUR CHIEF SAID WE WERE GOING TO THROW THEM BACK IN THE SEA IF...
NO, HE TOLD US TO TELL HIM WHAT THEY WERE DOING!
10A

MEANWHILE...
LOOK, JUSTFORKIX, WHY DON'T YOU GO BACK TO THE BEACH AND HAVE FUN INSTEAD OF HANGING ABOUT HERE?
CLACK CLACK CLACK CLACK

BECAUSE-THERE-ARE-NOOORMANS ON THE BEACH!

O CHIEF VITALSTATISTIX, THE NORMANS ARE LANDING!
AAAAAAH!

...AND THEY'VE GOT EVER SUCH FUNNY NAMES... TEEHEE! THEY ALL END IN "AF"!
THAT'S RIGHT! THEIR CHIEF IS CALLED TIMANDAHAF!

HA, HA, HA! DID YOU HEAR THAT, GETAFIX, CACOFONIX, OPERATIX, ACOUSTIX, POLYFONIX, HARMONIX?
HOHO! HOHO!

CRAZY! THEY'RE CRAZY! I'D BETTER WARN THE OTHERS. THERE MUST BE SOMEONE SANE AMONG THIS LOT!
HAHAHA
HOHOHO!
10B

COME HERE, ALL OF YOU! LISTEN TO ME! COME HERE!
IT'S A NORMANDY LANDING! THEY'RE GOING TO PUT US ALL TO FIRE AND THE SWORD! THERE ARE LOTS AND LOTS AND LOTS OF THEM! IT'S GOING TO BE A NORMAN CONQUEST!
WHAT'S HE ON ABOUT?
IT MUST BE SOME SORT OF LUTETIAN CUSTOM...
THE THING IS, I'VE GOT A BOAR COOKING...
NORMANS?
ATTACKING!
LET ME BY, WILL YOU?
STOP PUSHING!
THEY'VE GOT THE MESSAGE AT LAST... THEY'RE PANICKING! WELL, THAT'S NORMAL WHEN THE NORMANS ATTACK! WE'LL ESCAPE TOGETHER!
WAIT A MINUTE...?

WHERE DO WE BOOK OUR NORMANS?
IF THERE'S GOING TO BE A FIGHT I WANT MY SHARE!
I WISH TO MAKE A RESERVATION! LAST TIME WE FOUGHT THE ROMANS I DIDN'T GET A SINGLE ONE!
CALM DOWN! CALM DOWN, DO! I'M NOT TOO PLEASED THE NORMANS ARE HERE, BUT WE DON'T KNOW WHAT THEY WANT YET... IF THERE'S GOING TO BE A FIGHT YOU'LL ALL BE INFORMED IN GOOD TIME... SO NOW GO HOME, WOULD YOU?

AND NOW THINGS ARE A LITTLE QUIETER, HOW ABOUT THE HIT I'D MAKE IN LUTETIA...?

IN THE NORMAN CAMP, OLAF TIMANDAHAF IS JUST FINISHING A SOLE IN CREAM SAUCE...
NESCAF, I WANT YOU TO GO SCOUTING... SPY OUT THE LAND, SEE WHAT SORT OF PEOPLE THESE GAULS ARE!
RIGHT, O CHIEF TIMANDAHAF!

OUR VOYAGES ARE VERY EDUCATIONAL... WE LEARN ABOUT THE NATIVES BEFORE WE SLAUGHTER THEM.

I THINK I'LL HIDE IN THIS FOREST.

I'LL BE ALL RIGHT HERE... HULLO, THERE'S SOMEONE COMING...

WHAT DO YOU THINK THE NORMANS ARE GOING TO DO, ASTERIX?
WHO CARES? THEY WON'T SCARE US... WE DON'T KNOW THE MEANING OF FEAR! WE'VE NEVER BEEN FRIGHTENED OF ANYONE YET!

OH NO! WE'VE COME ALL THIS WAY FOR NOTHING...

HULLO, JUSTFORKIX? COMING TO HUNT BOAR WITH US?
HOW DO YOU LUTETIANS HUNT BOAR? HEREABOUTS WE JUST THUMP THEM AND THEN...

NO, I WANT TO ASK YOU A FAVOUR ... LOOK, THE CLIMATE HERE DOESN'T AGREE WITH ME TOO WELL. WILL YOU HELP ME PERSUADE MY UNCLE TO LET ME GO HOME TO LUTETIA...?
YOU'RE FRIGHTENED OF THE NORMANS, AREN'T YOU?

YEEEEES! I'M SO FRIGHTENED! I'M MORE FRIGHTENED THAN ANYONE ELSE IN THE WORLD! BOOHOOOOOOO!

YOU MUSTN'T BE FRIGHTENED, JUSTFORKIX... HAVE NO FEAR, WE'RE WITH YOU... NOW, YOU CAN'T BE FRIGHTENED WITH US HERE, CAN YOU?
SNIFF! NO, I DON'T FEEL SO FRIGHTENED NOW...

SPOILSPORT!

TIMANDAHAF IS JUST FINISHING HIS VEAL IN CREAM SAUCE...
OH, SO YOU'RE BACK, NESCAF. WHAT NEWS?

I'VE BEEN LISTENING TO SOME OF THE GAULS. THEY DON'T KNOW THE MEANING OF FEAR EITHER.

WHAT? YOU MEAN WE'VE COME ALL THIS WAY FOR NO GOOD REASON?
CRACK!

I'VE A GOOD MIND TO PUT US ALL TO THE SWORD... MAYBE WE'LL LEARN THE REASON* FOR FEAR AT ODIN'S FEAST,* SINCE THESE GAULS ARE SO IGNORANT!
THEY DO AS GOOD A SOLE* AS WE COULD GET FROM OUR OWN ICE FLOES,* THOUGH...
*SENTIMENTS ECHOED CENTURIES LATER BY ALEXANDER POPE...'THE FEAST OF REASON AND THE FLOW OF SOUL...'

ANYWAY, DON'T BOOK OUR TABLE YET! I DID HERE ONE GAUL BOAST HE WAS AN EXPERT ON FEAR...

A REAL PROFESSIONAL, BY THOR! THAT'S WHAT WE NEED!
THE ONLY THING IS, WHEN HE'S WITH THE OTHER GAULS HE ISN'T SO FRIGHTENED...

GET AN EXPEDITIONARY FORCE TOGETHER! WE MUST CAPTURE HIM AND SHIELD HIM FROM THE DEBILITATING INFLUENCE OF HIS FRIENDS!

FEAR WILL LEND US WINGS, AND WE'LL SOON BE AIRBORNE... HAVE A LITTLE SKULL NESCAF?
I WON'T SAY NO... LET'S PUT OUR HEADS TOGETHER.

MEANWHILE, IN THE GAULISH VILLAGE...
I... I'VE DECIDED TO CUT MY HOLIDAY SHORT AND GO BACK TO LUTETIA...
WHAT, JUST WHEN THE REAL FUN'S STARTING? OH, DON'T GO, JUSTFORKIX! YOU'LL LEARN HOW TO FIGHT! WE GAULS NEVER GIVE QUARTER!

I PROMISE YOU THERE WON'T BE ANY GAULISH QUARTER!
I KNOW, BUT THERE'S A LATIN QUARTER AND I'D LIKE TO GET BACK TO IT!
13

YOU'RE QUITE SURE, JUSTFORKIX? MUST YOU REALLY GO?
WAIT A MINUTE, JUSTFORKIX! I'VE GOT A LITTLE PRESENT FOR YOU!

A PRESENT FROM ARMORICA

WELL, IT'S A PITY... YOUR FATHER WANTED ME TO TOUGHEN YOU UP A BIT... RUB THE CORNERS OFF YOU...

I WISH I COULD GO TO LUTETIA TOO...

CORNERS... CORNERS...HUH! I CAN CUT A FEW CORNERS MYSELF!
A PRES FROM

CRAAACK!
?

BOTHER THAT MENHIR! IT'S GONE AND BROKEN THE AXLE... I'M IN A TIGHT CORNER NOW! THE TROUBLE WITH THESE FOREIGN CHARIOTS IS GETTING SPARE PARTS...
A PRES FROM

AND CLOSE AT HAND.
WHAT A BIT OF LUCK! IT'S THE MAN WHO KNOWS THE MEANING OF FEAR! WE MUST GRAB HIM BEFORE HE FLIES AWAY!
NOW REMEMBER, EVERYONE, THE CHIEF SAID TO BRING HIM BACK ALIVE!
ALL THESE LITTLE SUBTLETIES!
14

BY THOR!
BY ODIN!
OH MY GODS! THE NORMANS!

LEAVE ME ALONE! LEAVE ME ALONE, OR ASTERIX AND OBELIX WILL GET YOU!

ASTERIX? OBELIX? WHO ARE THEY?
THEY'RE VERY FIERCE! EVERYONE TREMBLES BEFORE THEM!

TREMBLES?
PEOPLE TREMBLE WHEN THEY'RE COLD!
OR WHEN THEY GET MARSH FEVER IN THE SUMMER.

NO, NO, YOU DON'T UNDERSTAND! PEOPLE TREMBLE WHEN THEY'RE FRIGHTENED! LOOK AT ME! I'M FRIGHTENED, AND...

QUICK! HE'S GOING TO FLY AWAY!

MERCY!

MERCY? WHAT'S THAT?
OH, NEVER MIND, IT'S ANOTHER OF THESE NEW INVENTIONS. BASH HIM OVER THE HEAD, BUT...

... NOT TOO HARD!
PAFF!

I HOPE YOU HAVEN'T CRACKED HIS SKULL... THE CHIEF DOESN'T LIKE CHIPPED GLASSES.
NO, WE DON'T WANT HIM ANY THE WORSE FOR LIQUOR.
WHEN I BASH SOMEONE, I BASH THEM!

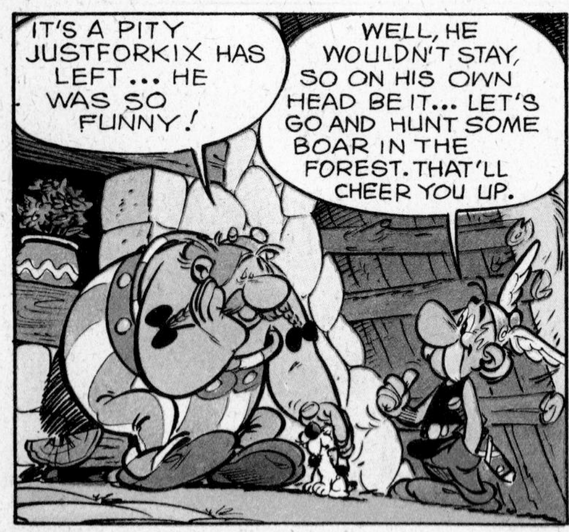
IT'S A PITY JUSTFORKIX HAS LEFT... HE WAS SO FUNNY!
WELL, HE WOULDN'T STAY, SO ON HIS OWN HEAD BE IT... LET'S GO AND HUNT SOME BOAR IN THE FOREST. THAT'LL CHEER YOU UP.

I DO LIKE IT IN THE FOREST... WE MIGHT FIND BOARS, ROMANS, MUSHROOMS, MAYBE EVEN NORMANS...

I TELL YOU WHAT, IF WE FIND ANY BOARS, ROMANS OR NORMANS WE KNOCK THEM ON THE HEAD, IF WE FIND ANY MUSHROOMS WE...
LOOK, DOGMATIX HAS STOPPED! HE'S PICKED UP A SCENT!
SNIFF SNIFF

LET'S FOLLOW HIM!
RIGHT. IF IT'S A BOAR WE'LL SHARE IT, IF IT'S A ROMAN OR A NORMAN YOU CAN LEAVE IT TO ME, IF IT'S A MUSHROOM I'LL LEAVE IT TO...

OH!

JUSTFORKIX'S CHARIOT!
ISN'T DOGMATIX MARVELLOUS? I TAUGHT HIM TO PICK UP THE SCENT OF A MENHIR, SO HE'D MADE A GOOD HOUND...
SNIFF SNIFF

I THOUGHT I'D START WITH MENHIRS BECAUSE THEY DON'T MOVE AS FAST AS RABBITS...
THE AXLE'S BROKEN...

FLIMSY, I CALL IT. IT MAY BE FAST, BUT IT'S FLIMSY. PUT ONE TINY LITTLE MENHIR IN IT, AND SOMETHING BREAKS!
I CAN'T SEE JUSTFORKIX GOING OFF INTO THE FOREST ALONE...

NO, HE'D HAVE TAKEN THE MENHIR WITH HIM!
FOOT PRINTS... I'M AFRAID THE NORMANS MAY HAVE KIDNAPPED JUSTFORKIX!

LET'S TELL CHIEF VITALSTATISTIX!
YOU MEAN THEY WANTED A SOUVENIR, THEY FOUND JUSTFORKIX AND MY MENHIR AND THEY TOOK JUSTFORKIX? THESE NORMANS ARE CRAZY!

IN THE NORMAN CAMP, WHERE TIMANDAHAF IS JUST FINISHING A CHICKEN IN CREAM SAUCE...
WE GOT HIM, O TIMANDAHAF!
BY ODIN! LET'S GO AND SEE HIM RIGHT AWAY, O NESCAF!

HE DOESN'T LOOK TOO GOOD, NESCAF!
WE CLUBBED HIM TO STOP HIM FLYING AWAY, THE WAY WE CLUB BIRDS... NOT VERY TOUGH, THIS GAULISH RIFFRAFF!
COMING!
NO, NO ONE WANTS YOU, RIFFRAF!

RIGHT. BRING HIM ROUND. COME HERE, ALL! MAKE HASTE!

SPLASH!
HASTING'S THE WORD...
SURELY IT'S NOT 1066 YET?

WHO... WHAT...?
HELP!

BY TOUTATIS, THIS IS THE END OF ME! ALL THESE NORMANS... SO MANY OF THEM! THEY LOOK SO FIERCE... HELP! THEY'RE GOING TO KILL ME... THEIR CHIEF IS COMING TOWARDS ME...

GO ON, THEN! FRIGHTEN US!
17

WH... WHAT DID YOU SAY?
I SAID: FRIGHTEN US!

WE'VE COME A VERY LONG WAY TO LEARN THE MEANING OF FEAR, SO GO AHEAD AND FRIGHTEN US!

NO, NO, YOU'VE GOT IT ALL WRONG! YOU FRIGHTEN ME!
I DO?
?

HOW CAN I FRIGHTEN YOU WHEN I DON'T KNOW THE MEANING OF FEAR?

YOU MEAN YOU FEEL FEAR NOW?
YES... I'M IN A COLD SWEAT, MY HEAD'S SWIMMING, MY STOMACH'S CHURNING...
18A

IT'S 'FLU. FEAR IS 'FLU.
DID YOU EVER SEE ANYONE WITH 'FLU WHO FLEW, BY ODIN?

COME ALONG, GAUL ... FRIGHTEN ME SO I CAN FLY A BIT!
WHAT ARE YOU TALKING ABOUT?

VERY WELL, IF YOU WON'T CO-OPERATE WE'LL THROW YOU OFF A CLIFF TOP TOMORROW! YOU'LL HAVE TO GIVE US A DEMONSTRATION OF YOUR POWERS AND FLY THEN!

NO, NO! PLEASE! I'M SO FRIGHTENED!
GNGNGN! HE'S REALLY GETTING ME DOWN! TIE HIM UP, SO HE CAN'T FLY AWAY OVERNIGHT.

THEY'RE CRAZY! ABSOLUTELY CRAZY! IF I EVER SEE LUTETIA AGAIN, THE LADS WILL NEVER BELIEVE ME!
BANG! BANG!
18B

JUSTFORKIX, KIDNAPPED? WELL, HE MAY NOT BE A VERY DUTIFUL SON AND NEPHEW... BUT WHY WOULD THEY KIDNAP HIM?
PERHAPS THEY WANTED SOME DUTY-FREE GOODS TO TAKE HOME.

ASTERIX AND OBELIX, GO OFF TO THE NORMAN CAMP AND SEE IF JUSTFORKIX IS THERE!

I'VE MADE YOU A LITTLE MAGIC POTION JUST IN CASE, ASTERIX.
THANKS, O GETAFIX.

I...
NO! YOU KNOW YOU'VE BEEN STRONG ENOUGH TO UPROOT A TREE SINCE YOU FELL IN THE POTION AS A BABY!

NO, HONESTLY! THE EFFECTS HAVE WORN OFF... WATCH THIS...

TEEHEE! I'M GOING TO PRETEND I CAN'T UPROOT A TREE AND THEN HE'LL GIVE ME SOME POTION! CUNNING, EH? TEEHEE!

LOOK! ARE YOU ALL WATCHING?
WE'RE WATCHING!

CREEEAK!
!?!

I UPROOT IT EVEN WHEN I'M ONLY PRETENDING!
??
HAHAHAHA!
BOOHOOHOOO!

WHAT'S THE MATTER WITH HIM?
DOGMATIX DOESN'T LIKE PEOPLE HURTING TREES... HE LOVES TREES... I WON'T DO IT AGAIN, DOGMATIX, I PROMISE!
SNIFF!
19

WE'RE GETTING CLOSE TO THE NORMAN CAMP... IF THEY TRY TO STOP US WE JUST WADE INTO THEM AND EXPLAIN LATER, RIGHT?
VERY CUNNING. COULDN'T HAVE THOUGHT OF A MORE SUBTLE PLAN MYSELF...

HALT! WHAT ARE YOU DOING HERE, GAULS?

WE WANT TO SEE YOUR CHIEF AND...

HOLD ON A MINUTE! YOU SAID WE'D JUST WADE INTO THEM AND EXPLAIN LATER!
BUT I HAVE TO TELL THEM WHY WE'RE HERE! THEN MAYBE WE WON'T HAVE TO WADE INTO THEM!

20A
WELL, I WON'T STAND FOR IT! A PLAN IS A PLAN! I AGREED TO YOUR PLAN IN EVERY DETAIL, AND...
OBELIX, YOU'RE GETTING ON MY NERVES!

COME HERE, EVERY-ONE! HERE'S A SPOT OF GAULISH CUISINE FOR ODIN'S FEAST!

BY THOR!
BY ODIN!
CHARGE!

RIGHT, NOW WE CAN WADE INTO THEM!
I SHOULD THINK SO TOO!
WOOF

20B
I KNEW YOU'D SEE SENSE IN THE END!
TCHAC!
DON'T LET'S ARGUE IN PUBLIC, OBELIX!

TCHAC!
CLONK!

THEY'VE GOT A BIT MORE BODY THAN THE ROMANS, WOULDN'T YOU SAY, ASTERIX?
NOT SO WELL ORGANIZED, BUT TOUGHER... AND THEY DON'T KNOW THE MEANING OF FEAR.
WOOF

DO YOU MIND KEEPING QUIET WHILE WE FIGHT?
BE SEEING YOU!
TAP TAP

AWFULLY SORRY!
PAF!
21A

BANG!
PAF!
TWEET! TWEET!
APPLE BRANDY

DRINK THIS, FOTOGRAF!

TCHAC!
BING!
BY ODIN AND-HIC-BY THOR!
APPLE BRANDY

HIC!
POC!
DID YOU SEE THAT? LOOKS AS IF THEY'VE GOT SOME KIND OF MAGIC POTION TOO!
YOU BET THEY HAVE! EVERYONE'S KNOCKING IT BACK EXCEPT ME!

NOT FAR AWAY, A PATROL IS MAINTAINING THE PAX ROMANA IN THIS FAR-FLUNG CORNER OF THE ROMAN EMPIRE...
YOU THERE... THE NEW RECRUIT! WHY THE FLOWERS?
IT'S MY FIRST PATROL!
SEND HIM ROUND TO THE OPTIO FOR A HANDFUL OF HALF-UNCIA HOLES!
THAT'S AN OLD ONE; THAT IS!
21B

PAF!
BY ODIN!
BING!
BY TOUTATIS!
BOOM!
BY THOR!
TCHAC!
BY BELENOS!
PATROL... HALT!
CLING!
CLONG!
CLANG!

HEAR THAT, CONSENSUS?
THEY'RE FIGHTING ON THE BEACHES!
PSST! DO WE PRESENT ARMS NOW?

COME ON!

?!?

WELL, OLEAGINUS? TRYING TO BE CLEVER?
N... NO, DECURION... I JUST THOUGHT WE WERE MAKING FOR THE BEACH...
POF!
POF!
22A

YOU'RE IN THE ARMY NOW! IT'S TIME YOU LEARNT OBEY ORDERS! WE KNOW HOW THE LAND LIES AND WE'RE GOING BACK TO CAMP TO TELL OUR SUPERIOR OFFICERS!!!

TELL THEM WHAT? WE DIDN'T GO DOWN TO THE BEACH, SO WE HAVEN'T SEEN ANYTHING!

AND JULIUS CAESAR SAID...
NEVER MIND WHAT JULIUS CAESAR SAID... NOT GOING AND NOT SEEING IS THE BEST WAY NOT TO GET CONQUERED!
POF!
PAF!
BING!

BACK IN THE ROMAN CAMP...
THREE SLABS OF MARBLE COMING UP, DECURION!
WHAT FOR?
FOR OUR REPORT IN TRIPLICATE... THERE'S A LOT OF MARBLE-WORK IN THE ARMY!
22B

*EAGER BEAVER. BUT DESPITE THE CASTOR ACTION FAVOURED BY OLEAGINUS, AMORICAN CAMPAIGNS SELDOM WENT ON OILED WHEELS.

COME ON, MEN! THEY'RE ATTACKING OUR DECURION!
HE'S NUTS!
THEY'LL LET JUST ANYONE JOIN THE ARMY THESE DAYS!

CHARRR!
TONK! TONK! TONK!
?
BONG!

PAF! PAF! PAF! PAF!
WHAT DO YOU MEAN BY YELLING AND GETTING IN PEOPLE'S WAY LIKE THAT? WHAT DO YOU MEAN BY IT, EH?
?

HERE, WHAT ABOUT ME?
?

OH, WOULD YOU LIKE A GO!
OO, CAN I REALLY?
?

24A
FAIR SHARES! WE'LL SPLIT HIM DOWN THE MIDDLE.
POC!
VERY GOOD OF YOU!

THANKS TO THESE TIMELY REINFORCEMENTS, THE BATTLE RAGES HARDER THAN EVER...
LEAVE US ALONE! LEAVE US ALONE!
WE'VE COME TO SETTLE YOUR QUARREL!
WE'RE A PEACE-KEEPING FORCE... WHY CLUB TOGETHER AGAINST US?
HIC!
APPLE BRANDY

BY ODIN, WHAT'S ALL THIS NOISE ABOUT? CAN'T A CHIEF EVEN EAT HIS BOAR IN CREAM SAUCE IN PEACE?

24B
BOAR IN CREAM SAUCE?

WHO ARE YOU, BY THOR, AND WHAT ARE YOU DOING WITH CARAF?
HEAR THAT, ASTERIX? MINE'S CALLED CARAF. WHAT ABOUT YOURS?
NO IDEA... WE HAVEN'T BEEN INTRODUCED.

BY ODIN, LET GO OF TELEGRAF AT ONCE, WILL YOU?
TELEGRAF, EH? PLEASED TO MEET YOU.

WHO ARE YOU?
MORE TO THE POINT, WHO ARE YOU?

I AM TIMANDAHAF THE CONQUEROR, CHIEF OF THE NORMANS!

SUCH FUNNY NAMES! HMMMMHEEHEEHO!
OBELIX, CONTROL YOURSELF! YOU'LL HURT HIS FEELINGS! REMEMBER OUR REPUTATION FOR GAULISH COURTESY...

WILL-YOU-KINDLY-TELL-ME-WHAT-YOU-WANT?
WE WANT TO ASK YOU SOME QUESTIONS.
POF! POF! POF! POF!

YES, HOW DO YOU MAKE THAT BOAR IN CREAM SAUCE?
WELL, IT'S JUST LIKE MAKING STRAWBERRIES AND CREAM, ONLY INSTEAD OF STRAWBERRIES YOU FIRST CATCH YOUR BOAR, THEN...

LOOK, YOU DIDN'T COME HERE AND ATTACK THE FIERCEST WARRIORS OF THE KNOWN WORLD JUST TO SWAP RECIPES, DID YOU?!?

NO, WE'VE GOT SOMETHING MORE IMPORTANT TO ASK YOU.
RIGHT, COME INTO MY TENT! STOP MAKING ALL THAT ROW, YOU LOT!
PAF! BING!

GOOD... WE WON'T KEEP YOU ANY LONGER... WE'RE OFF...
WE REALLY MUST BE GOING!
WE'RE DUE FOR SOME GAULISH LEAVE...
ALL GOOD THINGS COME TO AN END...
SSH! DIDN'T YOU HEAR WHAT YOUR CHIEF SAID?
25

MISSION ACCOMPLISHED, THE PATROL RETURNS TO CAMP...
WELL, SO WHAT'S GOING ON DOWN ON THE BEACH?
ON THE BEACH?
OH, NOTHING.
JUST A FEW BATHERS HAVING A LITTLE ARGUMENT...
IT'S ALL THIS THUNDER IN THE AIR...

AND YOU'LL BE GETTING A REPORT. IN TRIPLICATE...

MEANWHILE, IN THE TENT OF THE FEROCIOUS TIMANDAHAF...
HAVE YOU KIDNAPPED JUSTFORKIX?
YOUR EXPERT?
GRRRRR

EXPERT?
?

YOUR EXPERT KNOWS IT ALL, AND WE SHALL LEAVE ONCE HE'S TAUGHT US ALL HE KNOWS.

OH YES, HE'S AN EXPERT ON LUTETIAN DANCING... BUT I CAN TEACH YOU ABOUT ROCK MYSELF...

THIS IS THE WAY... ZING! ZOOM! ZING! ZOOM!

THEN YOU GO LIKE THIS... ZOOM! ZING! ZOOM! ZING!
LOOK, IS YOUR FRIEND MAKING FUN OF ME, FOOLING ABOUT LIKE THAT?
CLACK CLACK
CLACK CLACK

STOP IT, OBELIX. THE NORMANS DIDN'T COME HERE TO LEARN DANCING.
WELL, HE NEEDN'T THINK I'M DANCING ATTENDANCE ON HIM! FOOLING ABOUT, INDEED... BARBARIAN!

TEEHEEHEE! YOU SOUNDED JUST LIKE CACOFONIX THE BARD!
OH, VERY CLEVER!

WOULD YOU TWO MIND PAYING ATTENTION TO ME FOR A MOMENT?!?

SO WHAT KIND OF EXPERT IS YOUNG JUSTFORKIX?
AS IF YOU DIDN'T KNOW!

HE'S AN EXPERT ON FEAR, BY THOR! WE'RE COUNTING ON HIM TO TEACH US THE MEANING OF FEAR... WHETHER HE LIKES IT OR NOT!
???

AND IF HE WON'T WE'RE GOING TO THROW HIM OFF A CLIFFTOP TO WATCH HIM FLY!

ASTERIX, IF YOU ASK ME, THESE NORMANS ARE...
TAP TAP TAP
LET ME THINK A MOMENT, OBELIX.

IF WE TEACH YOU THE MEANING OF FEAR, WILL YOU GIVE US BACK OUR EXPERT AND GO AWAY?
YES. WE DIDN'T COME HERE TO MAKE WAR. WE'LL LEAVE THAT TO OUR DESCENDANTS A FEW CENTURIES FROM NOW...

WELL, WE'VE GOT SOMETHING IN OUR VILLAGE WHICH WILL DO THE TRICK. BUT WE'LL HAVE TO GO AND FETCH IT.
27A

ALL RIGHT, BUT ONE OF YOU STAYS HERE AS A HOSTAGE!

AND IF THE OTHER ONE DOESN'T COME BACK WE SHALL USE THE HOSTAGE'S SKULL FOR APPLE BRANDY!
PSSSPSSSPSSS!
GRRRRR

BUT WHY MUST I GO? YOU'LL HAVE ALL THE FUN! YOU'LL GET BOAR IN CREAM SAUCE! IT'S THE THOUGHT OF THAT APPLE BRANDY GOING TO YOUR HEAD...
STOP ARGUING, OBELIX. THIS ISN'T THE RIGHT MOMENT.

NOT THE RIGHT MOMENT! NOT THE RIGHT MOMENT! IT NEVER IS THE RIGHT MOMENT FOR MISTER ASTERIX...

I'M LANDED WITH ALL THE HARD WORK...
BOMM!

27B
HOOOWWWL! HOOOWL!
EVERYONE TAKES ADVANTAGE OF MY WEAKNESS!
CRAAAAASH!

HI, OBELIX!
HUH!
SNIF!

HEY, POLYTECHNIX, WHERE'S CACOFONIX? HE ISN'T AT HOME.
I'M GLAD TO SAY I HAVEN'T THE SLIGHTEST IDEA!

YOU'D BETTER GO AND ASK THE CHIEF, OBELIX.
HE'S LOOKING FOR THE BARD!
I THOUGHT HE WAS ACTING STRANGELY!

...AND IF I CAN'T FIND CACOFONIX, WHAT ABOUT ASTERIX AND JUSTFORKIX? WE CAN'T GIVE THE NORMANS THEIR HEADS! WE MUST DO SOMETHING!
BY TOUTATIS, LET'S HAVE A LOOK AT THE BARD'S HUT!

SOON AFTERWARDS.
HE'S TAKEN ALL HIS MUSICAL INSTRUMENTS AND NEARLY ALL HIS CLOTHES... HE REALLY HAS LEFT!

I NEVER THOUGHT WE'D BE SORRY TO SEE THE BACK OF OUR BARD... BUT NOW HE'S THE KEY TO OUR TROUBLES, HE'S OFF!
OFF KEY, AS USUAL!

I'VE GOT AN IDEA!
YOU HAVE, OBELIX?

DOGMATIX WILL FIND OUR BARD!
BUT, OBELIX...

DON'T YOU LISTEN TO THEM, DOGMATIX! SNIFF THIS! SEEK!
SNIFF! SNIFF!

POP!
POP!

SEE THAT, EH? SEE THAT? AT HIS AGE, TOO!
SNIFF! SNIFF! SNIFF! SNIFF!

BUT ISN'T THIS YOUR STOCKROOM, OBELIX?
SNIFF! SNIFF! GRRRRRR!

SO WHAT? HE FOLLOWED THE SCENT OF MENHIRS, THE WAY I TAUGHT HIM!
WELL, YOU'D BETTER START TEACHING HIM TO FOLLOW THE SCENT OF BARDS!
WOOF! WOOF!
OBELIX QUARRY

A HORSE HAS GONE!
IF CACOFONIX HAS TAKEN A HORSE HE MUST BE PLANNING A LONG JOURNEY!

I KNOW! THE ROLLING MENHIRS! THE PALACE OF VARIETIX! HE'S GONE TO LUTETIA!

I'M OFF AFTER HIM!
29
YOU KNOW, THAT LAD DOES HAVE HIS BRIGHT MOMENTS!

WHILE ASTERIX IS HELD HOSTAGE BY THE NORMANS...
OBELIX IS SURE TO COME BACK, TIMANDAHAF, NEVER FEAR!
WHAT DO YOU MEAN, NEVER FEAR??!!
FRESH CREAM

...OBELIX GOES TIRELESSLY ON IN PURSUIT OF CACOFONIX THE BARD...
NEVER MIND, DOGMATIX! I'LL TEACH YOU TO SNIFF OUT BARDS AND YOU'LL GROW INTO A BIG STRONG DOGGIE...

...PICKING THE ODD BOAR ALONG HIS WAY TO STILL THE PANGS OF HUNGER...
... WHAT A COUPLE WE SHALL MAKE, WITH MY BRAINS AND YOUR STRENGTH!

...AND CASUALLY ELIMINATING SUCH ROMAN PATROLS AS ARE MISGUIDED ENOUGH TO CROSS HIS PATH.
NO POINT IN STOPPING HIM... SOL LUCET OMNIBUS, AS WE SAY AT HOME. LET'S GO BACK AND CARVE A REPORT IN TRIPLICATE.
GETTING TO BE A REAL CHISELLER, AREN'T YOU?

WHOA THERE! CALM DOWN! STOP REARING! WHOA!
?

WE MET A MAN MAKING SUCH AWFUL NOISES MY OXEN STAMPEDED!

YOU SEE, WE MUST BE ON THE RIGHT TRACK, DOGMATIX! THIS IS THE WAY TO FOLLOW A BARD'S SCENT!

OH YES, I SAW A HORSEMAN GO BY, BUT THE WAY HE WAS SINGING HE CAN'T HAVE BEEN A BARD!

MOOoooo!
OH YES, HE CAME THIS WAY. THE MILK TURNED JUST THEN!

AND FURTHER ON...
CACOFONIX'S HORSE! WE'VE FOUND HIM! YOU SEE, DOGMATIX, THERE'S NO DIFFERENCE BETWEEN BARDS AND MENHIRS!
SELFSERVIX

SELFSERVIX
CACOFONIX! IT'S US! YOOHOO!

CACO... ???

ER... DO YOU HAPPEN TO HAVE SEEN A BARD, MR... ER...?
SELFSERVIX, AT YOUR SERVICE... OH YES, I'VE SEEN A BARD ALL RIGHT, BY TOUTATIS!

HE COULDN'T PAY FOR THE MEAL HE ATE, HE SUGGESTED SINGING FOR HIS SUPPER ONCE HE STARTED I TOLD HIM IT WAS ON THE HOUSE...

... AND MY CUSTOMERS EVEN OFFERED HIM ANOTHER MEAL TO SHUT UP... SO HE GOT ANNOYED ... AND NOW THE HOUSE IS ON ME!
SOBS

HE LEFT ME HIS HORSE AS COMPENSATION...
WELL, IF CACOFONIX IS GOING TO PAY HIS WAY BY SINGING HE WON'T GET FAR!

THERE HE IS!

CACOFONIX! YOOHOO! WAIT FOR US!
HA! I KNEW IT! THEY CAN'T DO WITHOUT ME IN THE VILLAGE. TOO BAD! I'VE GOT MY CAREER TO THINK OF!
31

CACOFONIX, I'VE BEEN LOOKING FOR YOU TO...
THE ANSWER IS NO! YOU DON'T APPRECIATE MY ART! WELL, YOU CAN JUST DO WITHOUT ME, SO THERE! I'M GOING TO BE A HIT IN LUTETIA!

LISTEN, ASTERIX SENT ME! HE NEEDS YOU!
ASTERIX HAS NO MORE MUSICAL FEELING THAN ALL THE REST OF YOU, BUT HE'S A GOOD BIT CLEVERER. HE WON'T BE NEEDING ME!

...AND JUSTFORKIX IS IN DANGER!
JUSTFORKIX?

JUSTFORKIX? THAT DISCERNING YOUNG MAN IN TROUBLE?
YES, THE NORMANS ARE UP TO SOME KIND OF SKULDUGGERY...

OH, I SEE! YOU WANT ME TO SOOTHE THEIR SAVAGE BREASTS... VERY WELL, THEN! OFF WE GO!
?

I MIGHT AS WELL MAKE A TOUR OF THE PROVINCES BEFORE I HIT LUTETIA!
TAP! TAP! TAP!

THIS OLD MAN, HE PLAYED UNUM...

ER... CACOFONIX... COULD WE DO WITHOUT A SONG? YOU SEE, IT'S DOGMATIX, HE...
NO, WE COULD NOT IF YOU WANT MY SIREN SONG, I'M GOING TO SING, AND THAT'S MY LAST WORD!

THIS OLD MAN, HE PLAYED DUO...
COME ALONG, BRAVE LITTLE DOGS DON'T CRY, DOGMATIX! YOU WANT OBELIX TO BE PROUD OF YOU, DON'T YOU?
BOO HOO!

AT ALL EVENTS, THE BARD'S SIREN SONG CLEARS THE ROADS FOR OUR GAULISH FRIENDS...
WATCH OUT! MY OXEN ARE BOLTING!

...ONE OF WHOM IS TURNING THE MILK BEFORE TURNING HIS AUDIENCE'S HEADS.
MOOOO!
VANDALS!
THIS OLD MAN, HE PLAYED CENTUM QUINQUAGINTA SEPTEM...

THINGS ARE GOING FROM BAD TO WORSE IN THE NORMAN CAMP...
THESE SAUSAGES IN CREAM SAUCE ARE VERY GOOD!
SHUT UP, BY THOR!
BANG!

YOU'RE HAVING ME ON! I WON'T WAIT ANY LONGER! THE HOSTAGES WILL BE EXECUTED! SOMEONE GO AND GET THE GAULISH EXPERT OFF THE LONGSHIP!

LONGSHIP?
ONE OF OUR VESSELS. WE CAN USE EITHER SAIL OR OARS.

I KNEW YOUR FAVOURITE SPORT WAS SCULLING!
PUT THIS ONE IN CHAINS AND TAKE THEM BOTH UP THE CLIFF!

SOON AFTERWARDS...
I DON'T KNOW WHAT'S KEEPING OBELIX, BUT YOU MIGHT WAIT A LITTLE LONGER...
NO, I MIGHT NOT! YOU TWO HAVE A TABLE BOOKED FOR THE NEXT SITTING AT ODIN'S BANQUET!

BUT FIRST, IN THE CAUSE OF SCIENCE, YOU'RE GOING TO FLY OFF THIS CLIFF!
WOULDN'T YOU RATHER I GROVELLED AT YOUR FEET?

CHEER UP, JUSTFORKIX! SHOW THESE NORMANS HOW BRAVELY A GAUL CAN DIE!
YOU WAIT, THEY HAVEN'T FINISHED THEIR FUN YET!

RIGHT, I WANT YOU TO FLY OVER THERE TO THE LEFT. AFTER THAT I WANT YOU TO...
DON'T WORRY ABOUT THE ROUTE. IT'S NON-STOP, DIRECT...
33

GO ON, GAUL, FLY!
I COULDN'T POSSIBLY!

NO, REALLY! HONESTLY I COULDN'T! OUT OF THE QUESTION!
NOT VERY CO-OPERATIVE, ARE THEY... HEY, YOU TWO!

WITH A ONE...
NO! NO! NOOO!
AND A TWO...

AND A THR...
JUST A MOMENT!

IF I FRIGHTEN YOU... YOU... YOU WON'T MAKE ME FLY?
OF COURSE NOT! WE'LL BE FLYING FROM YOU!

ALL RIGHT, THEN! I'LL FRIGHTEN YOU!
SO THE GAULS HAVE DECIDED TO BE AS REASONABLE AS US! GATHER ROUND, EVERYONE!

FIRST I'M GOING TO TELL YOU A DREADFUL STORY ABOUT SOME OGRES WHO KILLED A LOT OF...
HMM... LIKE THE TIME I DID IN 24 ENEMIES AT A GO BECAUSE I WANTED TO GIVE A SET OF SKULLS TO A FRIEND FOR A WEDDING PRESENT...

...ONLY HE WASN'T TOO PLEASED... EVERYONE ELSE HAD THE SAME IDEA! OUR ENEMIES COULDN'T MAKE HEAD OR TAIL OF IT! HA! HA! HA! HA! HA! HA!
HO!
HO!
HO! HO! HO! HO!

BOO!
?

AAAAAARRRRGHH!
EEEK!

?
?
?
?
?
?
?

HO!HO!HO!
TEEHEE HEE!
HA!HA!HA!

HA!HA!HA!
HO!HO!HO!

HOU!HOU!
HO!HO!
HA!
YOU'RE NOT BEING ANY HELP, ASTERIX! I WAS MAKING THOSE FACES TO FRIGHTEN THEM!
TEEHEEHEE!

HO! HO! HO!
WHEN I USED TO MAKE FACES LIKE THAT AT HOME MY LITTLE SISTER WAS VERY FRIGHTENED, AND...
YOU KNOW, LITTLE SISTERS USUALLY SCARE MORE EASILY THAN BIG BARBARIANS.

WELL, THAT'S ENOUGH JOKING. LET'S GET BACK TO BUSINESS. NOW FOR YOUR FLYING DEMONSTRATION!

FIRSTHAF! SECONDHAF! TAKE HIM OVER TO THE RUNWAY!

IS THIS ALL RIGHT?
OH, I'M SO FRIGHTENED!

HE'S IN FINE FORM FOR FLYING NOW ... CAN HE TAKE OFF?
CHATTER! CHATTER!

ALL SYSTEMS GO! I REPEAT, ALL SYSTEMS GO! I ...
JUST A MOMENT! GNGNGN!

TCHAC!

WE'RE NOT GIVING IN WITHOUT A FIGHT!
JUSTFORKIX... CHARGE!
35

TCHAC!

I DON'T WANT THE EXPERT DAMAGED. CONCENTRATE ON THE LITTLE ONE, BY THOR!

LET HIM GO! LET HIM GO, I TELL YOU! YOU JUST LET HIM GO!
BONG! BONG! BONG! BONG!

POFF!

THAT LITTLE GAUL IS REALLY PRETTY GOOD!

?
POFF!

FUNNY, I DIDN'T KNOW THERE WAS AN ECHO UP HERE...

!
YOOHOO! IT'S US, ASTERIX!
36

OBELIX! AT LAST!
WOOF!
NOW WHAT? DO WE STOP OR DO WE CARRY ON? NOW WHAT?
WHERE'S THE OTHER ONE GONE? THE EXPERT?
BONG! BONG! BONG!

YOU TOOK YOUR TIME ALL RIGHT! YOU KNOW, I WAS BEGINNING TO GET WORRIED, ALL ON MY OWN...
I CAN EXPLAIN, ASTERIX. IT WAS LIKE THIS...

HERE, ARE YOU TWO STARTING TO CHAT AGAIN? HAVE YOU BROUGHT ME THIS AMAZING THING YOU MENTIONED?

HERE YOU ARE!
WHAT, HIM?!
IN PERSON.

HO!HO!HO!HO!

ALL RIGHT, I GET THE MESSAGE. I'M OFF.
HA!HA! TEEHEEHE!
?
!

WAIT A MINUTE, CACOFONIX!
I WARN YOU, ASTERIX, I'M NOT PERFORMING FOR PHILISTINES WHO DON'T KNOW THE SCORE!

YOU WAIT THERE WITH YOUR MEN. I'LL BE BACK DIRECTLY.
ALL RIGHT. TEEHEEHEE! YOU REALLY ARE A LAUGH, YOU LOT!

NOW, THESE PEOPLE HAVE COME A LONG, LONG WAY TO HEAR OUR TRADITIONAL GAULISH MUSIC! YOU'RE NOT GOING TO DISAPPOINT THEM, ARE YOU?

A RECITAL? A SOLO PERFORMANCE? WHAT A RESPONSIBILITY!... BUT HOW ARE THE ACOUSTICS UP ON THIS CLIFF? ACOUSTICS ARE MOST IMPORTANT... IF THE ACOUSTICS ARE BAD I COULDN'T DREAM OF IT!

WELL, AM I READY TO GIVE THEM A FEW NUMBERS?
I HOPE SO! IF NOT, OUR NUMBER'S UP! I'LL ANNOUCE YOU.
37

NORMANS, FOR THE VERY FIRST TIME OUR BARD CACOFONIX IS ABOUT TO APPEAR BEFORE YOU IN A SOLO PERFORMANCE!

SOMETHING TELLS ME IT'S THE VERY LAST TIME TOO! HE'LL SOON BE FLYING SOLO!

HAHAHAHAHAHA

GO ON, CACOFONIX! SHOW THEM WHAT YOU CAN DO!

THE AUDIENCE NEEDS WARMING UP A BIT...
PTOIIISING!
TOIIING!

I LOVE A LASSIE, A BONNIE GAULISH LASSIE, SHE'S AS FAIR AS THE BOARS ROUND THE DOLMEN...

GET WITH IT! I'M REAL GONE!
OOOOH!
HELP!
OUCH! OUCH!
OW! OW! OW!
38

I LIKE TO BE IN ARMORICA... ROCK AROUND THE HOROLOGIUM...
OH YEAH!
TDZOIIIIING!
DZOOOOOONG!
TZIIIIIIING!

BY THOR!
BY ODIN!
BITE ON THE BULLET!

IT'S WORKING! IT'S WORKING!
BONG! BONG!

WHAT DID YOU SAY?
?
POP!

STOP! STOP!

WHAT WAS THAT?
ENCORE! ENCORE!

SILENCE, PLEASE! OUR BARD WILL NOW GIVE YOU A MEDLEY OF ALL HIS RECENT HITS!
OH YEAH!
TZONG!

NO! NO! BY ODIN! ANYTHING, BUT NOT THAT!

WHY NOT, MAY I ASK?
THE MERE IDEA OF HEARING HIM AGAIN MAKES MY KNEES KNOCK AND MY TEETH CHATTER; I'M IN A COLD SWEAT AND MY STOMACH IS CHURNING...

IN FACT: YOU KNOW THE MEANING OF FEAR!

FEAR? YOU MEAN I'M FRIGHTENED? WE'RE ALL FRIGHTENED?

WE'VE DONE IT! OUR EXPERIMENT HAS WORKED! WE KNOW THE MEANING OF FEAR! SO NOW THE NORMANS KNOW EVERYTHING! EVERYTHING!
BY ODIN AND BY THOR!

THANK YOU GAUL! COME TO MY ARMS!
NO FEAR!
WAIT A MOMENT!

WHERE DO I COME INTO ALL THIS? I DON'T KNOW WHAT YOU'RE ON ABOUT, BUT DO I CARRY ON WITH MY RECITAL OR NOT? WE DON'T WANT TO BREAK THE MOOD!

IT DOESN'T MATTER NOW! YOU'VE HAD A TRIUMPH! AN UNPRECEDENTED SUCCESS!
I HAVE?

ABSOLUTELY GREAT! CRAZY, MAN, CRAZY!
YOU MEAN I WAS GOOD?
FAN-TAS-TIC!

WELL, YOU KNOW, I DON'T DESERVE ANY CREDIT! WITH AN AUDIENCE LIKE THAT YOU FEEL YOU'RE SINGING FOR YOUR FRIENDS!
IF I HAD A SLAB OF MARBLE HANDY I'D ASK FOR YOUR AUTOGRAPH!
YES?
NO, NOT YOURS, AUTOGRAF!

AND WHAT DO YOU SAY, OBELIX, MY DEAR FELLOW?

WHAT WAS THAT AGAIN?
?

HOW CAN I EXPRESS MY GRATITUDE, GAUL?
WELL, YOU AND YOUR MEN COULD GO HOME IN YOUR LONGSHIP, NORMAN, AND STAY AWAY A FEW CENTURIES LONGER!

I CAN HARDLY WAIT TO GET HOME... ALL THOSE SCIENTIFIC CONFERENCES... BUT FIRST I WANT TO DO SOMETHING FOR YOU! YOU TAUGHT US THE MEANING OF FEAR!

SO WE SHALL HOLD A FAREWELL FEAST IN YOUR HONOUR, IN THE TRUE NORMAN FASHION...
OH, DON'T BOTHER! TO SAY GOODBYE IS TO DIET A LITTLE.

... WE'LL SLAUGHTER YOU ALL AND SEND YOU TO ODIN'S BANQUET IN VALHALLA! YOU'LL TASTE THE VERY LAST WORD IN NORMAN COOKING...

THE CRÈME DE LA CRÈME!
THAT'S ABOUT ENOUGH OF THAT! IF YOU'VE QUITE FINISHED...

... LET ME TELL YOU, YOU'VE OUTSTAYED YOUR WELCOME, THE PARTY'S OVER, SIC TRANSIT GLORIA AND ALL THAT! WE'RE SICK OF YOU AND WE'D LIKE TO SEE YOU IN TRANSIT! GET IT?
?
WELL, WELL, IF HE HASN'T LEARNT A BIT OF COURAGE!

THEM AND THEIR CONQUESTS! WE'LL NEVER HEAR THE END OF IT!
BUT I'VE MADE YOU AN OFFER YOU CAN'T REFUSE!

JUSTFORKIX IS RIGHT... THEY'RE A PAIN IN THE NECK!

WHAT?
A PAIN IN THE NECK!
POP

YES, OF COURSE HE'S A PAIN IN THE NECK, NOT TO MENTION THE EARS, BUT ALL YOU HAVE TO DO IS PUT PARSLEY IN THEM WHEN HE STARTS SINGING, SAME AS ME.
SIGH

NORMANS... CHARGE!

THE AUDIENCE MAY HAVE WARMED UP A BIT TOO MUCH...
COME ON, THEN! WHO WANTS TO HAVE A GO?
SNIFF SNIFF!
OO, ARE WE GOING TO FIGHT? REALLY? BUT WHAT FOR?
POP! POP!
I'LL EXPLAIN LATER.
41

COME ON, THEN! COME ON!
WE'LL HAVE TO ENGAGE SOME BOUNCERS FOR MY NEXT CONCERT!
SNIFF!
SNIFF!
SNIFF!
BONG!
BING!
TCHRAC!
BAONG!
PAF!
GRRRRR

NO!
WHAT DO YOU MEAN, NO?

ARE YOU RETREATING, NORMANS? BUT YOU NEVER RETREAT!

HE'S RIGHT, THEY'RE RETREATING! WHAT'S THE MATTER WITH THEM, ASTERIX?
THEY'RE FRIGHTENED, BY TOUTATIS! THANKS TO US, THEY KNOW THE MEANING OF FEAR!

FEAR... THAT'S IT!
MUMMY!
RUN FOR YOUR LIVES!
LET'S SKULK BACK HOME!

GIVE THEM A DIRGE TO SEE THEM OFF THE PREMISES.
WE'LL TAKE A SKULL OF KINDNESS YET...
TZINNNG!
DZONG!
DZING!

WELL, WE CAN FLY NOW, SO LET'S TAKE WING!
GET WITH IT! YOU'RE REAL GONE!
COME ON, THEN! COME ON!
WHAT'S BEEN GOING ON, ASTERIX?
OH, NOTHING TO MAKE A SONG ABOUT, OBELIX.
42

AFTER THEIR FIRST FLIGHT, WHICH IS SHORT AND SHARP, THE NORMANS REJOIN THEIR SHIP...

...BUT ONCE THEY ARE BACK ON BOARD, THINGS SOMEHOW SEEM DIFFERENT...
GET UP INTO THE CROW'S NEST, TOOCLEVERBYHAF!
THE TROUBLE IS...

WELL?
I FEEL SO FRIGHTENED UP THERE ALL ON MY OWN.

GET UP THAT MAST!
YES, CHIEF!
TCHIC!

EEEK!
CHIEF!

DON'T SNEAK UP BEHIND ME LIKE THAT! IT FRIGHTENS ME. WHAT DO YOU WANT?
IT'S THE MEN, CHIEF... THEY WANT YOU TO STOP SHOUTING LIKE THAT. IT FRIGHTENS THEM.

I FEAR OUR VOYAGE HAS BEEN ONLY TOO SUCCESSFUL...
SCRATCH! SCRATCH!

NEVER MIND, WE CAN FLY NOW...

FLY DOWN HERE, TOOCLEVERBYHAF!
YES, CHIEF!

SPLATCH!

YOU... YOU DON'T THINK THEY WERE HAVING US ON, CHIEF?
MAYBE, MAYBE NOT... ANYWAY, WE MUST BE CAREFUL IN FUTURE!
43

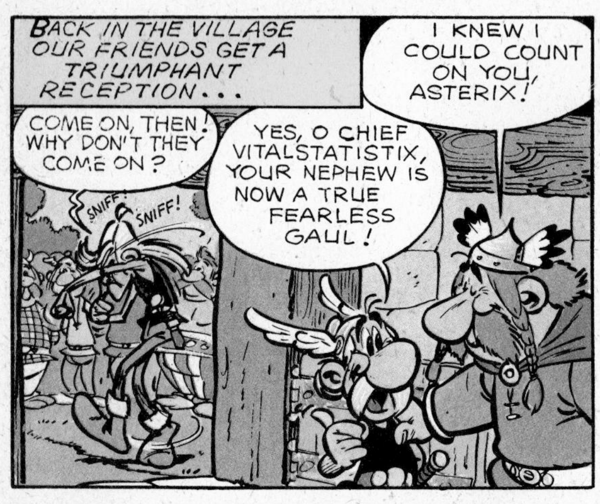

BACK IN THE VILLAGE OUR FRIENDS GET A TRIUMPHANT RECEPTION...
COME ON, THEN. WHY DON'T THEY COME ON?
SNIFF!
SNIFF!
YES, O CHIEF VITALSTATISTIX, YOUR NEPHEW IS NOW A TRUE FEARLESS GAUL!
I KNEW I COULD COUNT ON YOU, ASTERIX!

OBELIX TAKES JUSTFORKIX IN HAND...
I'LL TEACH YOU HOW TO HUNT... WE'LL START WITH RABBITS, GO ON TO ROMAN PATROLS, AND WORK OUR WAY UP TO WILD BOAR!

LIKE MANY OTHER STARS, THE BARD LIKES TO DESCRIBE HIS HITS...
THEY STAMPED, THEY JUMPED UP AND DOWN, THEY TRIED TO GET AT ME!
YOU SHOULD GO FAR... THE FARTHER THE BETTER.

O GETAFIX, DO YOU THINK THE NORMANS HAD THE RIGHT IDEA WHEN THEY WANTED TO KNOW THE MEANING OF FEAR?
OF COURSE, ASTERIX!

IT'S ONLY WHEN YOU KNOW FEAR THAT YOU BECOME TRULY BRAVE! COURAGE LIES IN OVERCOMING YOUR FEAR!

AND SURE ENOUGH, THE NORMANS HAVE FOUGHT THEIR FEAR AND OVERCOME IT. THEY ARE STILL BRAVE, AND THEIR TABLES ARE BOOKED IN VALHALLA!
I ONLY ASKED IF THEY'D MADE ANY GOOD CONQUESTS LATELY.
YOU MIGHT HAVE KNOWN THAT WAS A NORSE CHESTNUT!

AS FOR JUSTFORKIX, HIS HOLIDAY IN THE BRACING AIR OF ARMORICA IS OVER. THE TIME HAS COME FOR HIM TO GO HOME TO LUTETIA. THE VILLAGERS GIVE HIM A SPLENDID FAREWELL BANQUET, AND CACOFONIX IS INVITED, SINCE IT IS, AFTER ALL, THANKS TO THE BARD THAT ALL'S WELL THAT ENDS WELL...
OH YEAH!
UDERZO & GOSCINNY
THE END

PRINTED IN
proost Turnhout (Belgium)
PRINTED